... this book is dedicated to greyhounds
everywhere – to those that have been lucky
enough to find their forever homes, to those who
were never that lucky at all, and to those who
still have a chance.

Me Ritings: The Rather Luffly Journal of Davids Best Mate

Written by Becky Carr
Designed and produced by Nicki Porter

Published by Diverze Publishing - www.diverze-publishing.com
First Edition - Printed 2012 in Great Britain by Diverze Print - www.diverze-print.com

Me Ritings

The Rather Luffly Journal of
Davids Best Mate

Fings I's dun ritings about:

Happy New Year —————————— 1st Janury

I's cut me ear —————————— 29th Janury

Valentines powm —————————— 14th Febury

I's hexploding —————————— 24th Febury

Mousey —————————————— 1st March

Giraffe door —————————— 25th March

Eeaster bunny —————————— 4th April

Lampshade —————————————— 14th April

An introoder —————————— 10th May

Muvvas gotcha day —————————— 12th May

Me workings —————————— 11th Joon

Me teefs —————————————— 24th Joon

Hunt for me brindle ———————— 5th July

Boating for brindles ———————17th July

A barf! ————————————— 13th Orgust

Bump into walls ————————20th Orgust

Me t-shirt! ——————— 18th Septemba

Mummy's berfdie ———————28th Septemba

Me berfdie ————————————— 1st Octoba

Anuvva acsident! ———————— 20th Octoba

A goat! ——————————————— 3rd Novemba

Food feefery ———————— 23rd Novemba

Letter to Santa Claws ——————— 1st Decemba

Crismiss Day ————————— 25th Decemba

1st Janury

For Crismiss Santa Claws bort me a new diary. I woz qwite pleezed wiv me diary becoz I luffs to do me ritings. Normly, I duz me ritings on the compooter and puts them on me blog but I finks to meself that it wood be qwite good to puts me ritings in a little diary book insted.

I finks to praps tell you a bit abouts meself. I's David and I's a brindle greyhound. I used to do runnings really fast for me dinner but now I lives wiv me Mummy and I duz cleaning yogert pots for me dinners insted. I duz still do runnings really fast for me dinner tho, but I runs from the sofa to me bowls insted of running all the ways round a track.

I's got lots of favrit fings but me very best favrit is me duck! I luffs me duck very much and I duz frowing me duck and plucking me duck and killing me duck! I also luffs walkies and sqwirrels and wabbits and bouncing. And me uvva favrit fings are chikin and sardines and sosidges and cuddles and doing sleeping!

Becoz I's a luffly brindle colour, I gets qwite worried abouts me brindles washing off so I has to be qwite carefuls wen there's water about, speshally rain. I's already lost me brindle on me toes from having to do walkies through puddles!

arooooo
i luffs to do singing!

29th Janury

Last nite wen we's doing walkes, I's had an acsident. Mummy and I woz out on our walk wen I sees one of those wabbits wiv the long tails and short pointy ears. Well, I sees this wabbit and finks that I's going to go chase it but I woz on me leed and the wabbit runs into a bush. I puts me hed into the bush to sees where the wabbit went but it woz too qwick for me. Wen I takes me hed out of the bush I catch me ear on sumfing sharp. I screams qwite loud so that Mummy no's me ear's been ripped off and she gives me a big hug and we carries on our walk. It woz alrite carrying on, but me ear kept leeking red stuff and Mummy didn't seem to notice, so I has to do a bit of a dance and sqweek a bit to let Mummy no's that I's hurting a little. Mummy pats me on me hed and then see's that I's all red insted of me luffly brindle colour. I finks she's a bit worried abouts where me brindle is gone becoz she tries to wipe the red off wiv her coat and then her coat turns red too! Mummy sez that we has to get home qwickly becoz the red stuff is actually blood!

We's walking home qwite qwickly wen we see's me friends Phoebe and Brindley. I has to goes and sniffs their bottoms becoz they's me friends and I accidentally puts blood all over Phoebe's wite bits.

i's leeked red stuff all ova me luffly brindle!

Their Mummy starts trying to wash the blood off me so they can see's where I's leeking. Wen they see's it's me ear, me finks that Mummy is pleezed. Mummy sez she's pleezed I's not cut me hed open becoz of the rest of me brain falling out. Me finks to meself that it must be qwite good that I's kept me brain in.

Anyways, so we walks the rest of the way home, wiv me brain in me hed and me ear not leeking qwite as much. Wen we gets home Mummy sez to me to stay in the kitchen wot I duz, becoz I's a good boy. Wen I's being a good boy in the kitchen the blood starts tickling me as it runs down me face so I has a little shake, just to get rid of it a bit and it makes me feel all better for a little while. Wen Mummy comes back into the kitchen she sez it looks like a merder seen.. Me finks that it must be a good fing becoz Hooman Nanny cums ova and we did spending all evenin in the kitchen. We's not dun that before! It woz alrite being all that time in the kitchen but Mummy had to wrap me hed in a bandage to stop the leeking and that wozn't very cumfee.

Fankfully me ear has mostly stopped bleeding now. Wen I shakes me head it only leeks little bits and Mummy can just cleen them up wiv tissue. That means I's now not got any silly bandage on me hed. I's very pleezed.

me sad face!

14th Febury

I's hembarrassed to says that I's in luff
And I duznt gets to sees you nearly enuff
So I's doing me ritings to you this time
Me luffly brindle valentine.

You's brindle and luffly and really qwite fluffy
And wen I see's you me insides go all mushy!
Like sumtimes wot happens wen I eats too qwick
Sept wen I see's you I duznt be sick.

And wen we goes long walkies in the park
I tries to be qwiet and tries not to bark
Becoz I duznt wants to hembarrass you
Becoz you's very sensibles, its tru!

You's got luffly round eyes wot are very brown
And wen I sits of me frone and wears me crown
I finks to meself in me little brain
That I's looking forward to wen I sees them agen

So wen I's all curled up in me cozee nest bed
And resting me legs and me big brindle hed
I's finking abouts you all the time,
Me luffly brindle valentine.

me luffly ella!

24th Febury

I's feeling qwite sad today.

Last nite wen I woz fast asleeps, an angry hound got insides me belly and started doing growling at me! It made me feels like I needed to go poos qwite urgently. So me finks to meself to wake Mummy up really qwickly so I duz whinging and pawing but Mummy finks that I's just cold and wants bed cuddles so she sez to me to go away and be qwiet. I coodn't be a good boy and go aways and be qwiet tho becoz I needed to go toilet, so I duz whinging louder. Heventually Mummy gets up to go toilet and I races her to the door. Fankfully she lets me outside so I can go poos. I's qwite sprized tho becoz I finks I's about to do pooing wen suddenly I's hexploding! Me finks hexploding isnt good but it makes the angry hounds in me belly stop growling for little whiles so I's qwite pleezed bout that. I trots meself indoors and goes curls up on me bed.

Suddenly, wen Mummy and I's back asleeps, the angry hounds come back and me finks to meself that I need to go toilet agen. I duz whinging and pawing again but Mummy just sez to me that I's been for wees and to be qwiet. I trys to tell Mummy that I didnt *do wees and that I's actually hexploded but she sends me to me bed! Me finks to run up and down the stairs really qwickly doing whinging to makes Mummy get up, wot she duz and I goes to the door again. Mummy gets to the door just in time and I steps outside and the angry hound makes me do hexploding again very qwickly.*

i's poorly wiv me teddy

Mummy sees me do hexploding and sez she feels very bad that she didnt lissen to me whinging but she sez I's a good boy for keeping the hexplosion in for all that time!

The angry hounds made me do hexploding agen during the nite but Mummy knew that woz why I was doing whinging and gots up to let me go toilet very qwickly. I's hexploded on me walkies as well this morning and I's feeling qwite sad becoz Mummy sez I's not allowed any brekfst although she has sed that I's having chikin and rice for tea! I luffs chikin, its me favrit!

1st March

Last nite on me walkies I's dun lots of sniffing and snuffling! Wen we gots neerly home we see'd a cat! The cat woz in the passidj! I dun sqweeking and spinning becoz I wanted to plays wiv the cat but it dun running away! Wen the cat dun running away it dropped wot it had in its mouf! Wen we woz walking down the passidj, I finks to meself to look at wot the cat dropped so I duz sniffing it and it moved! It woz a mouse! Becoz Mummy takes fings out of me mouf wot I picks up on walkies I finks to meself to be qwite qwicks and eats the mouse very qwicky becoz I's not had me tea and I woz qwite hungry! So I picks up the mouse and and swallows him before Mummy cood call me 'leave'! Mummy sed 'yuk' insted but I finks that the mouse wasn't yuk, it was yummy. I finks to look for more mouses on walkies tomoro!

me noze!

25th March

We's had a new door put in the front room dis week. Mummy sez that it will stop the giraffes from coming in. I finks that I must do too much sleeping becoz I's never see'd any giraffes, sept sumtimes on the telly. Anyways, we's now got this door wot we's nevva had before that Mummy likes shut in the evenins (to keep the giraffes out).

In the evenins I likes to play wiv me duck and I runs about wiv it qwite a lot. So, I's frowing me duck about last nite and I finks that it wood be fun to run froo to the dining room wiv it and then run back again, like normal, wen suddenly I goes FUD! I's run strayt into the giraffe door. Fankfully, I's not really hurt but I do whining just in case and gives Mummy that look so I gets a big cuddle! I finks not to play wiv me duck for the rest of the evenin and duz sleepings in me bed.

The giraffe door

4th April

We waked up this morning and Mummy sez its Eester! I's not really sure wot Eester is but Mummy sez that a wabbit cums and brings me sum eggs. I duz luffs eggs. Mummy sez becoz the Eester Bunny has put sum eggs in the cold cubbord I can hav sum scrambled eggies for me brekfst. I woz qwite pleezed sept that I probly did sleeping through the wabbit being in me house. I wood likes to hav see'd the Eester Bunny.

Wen we goes walkies we meets sum of me frends. I woz pleezed becoz I duz luffs to see me frends too. I woz allowed off me leed to play wiv them so I dun sum running. We played chase. Sumtimes I dun chasing. Sumtimes I's had to be the wabbit. I duzn't luffs to be the wabbit qwite as much becoz they mite forgets that I's not a wabbit. I luffs to do chasing best.

Suddenly, wen we's playing chase I see's wiv me eyes, a WABBIT. I finks qwite qwickly to meself that it mite be the Eester Bunny so me finks to catch it so I can see's if it's got eggs. I chases after the wabbit and I runs really fast. All of a sudden the wabbit goes hinvizzible. I tries to stop very qwickly so I can see's if I can see's if the wabbit has unhinvizzibled. Hunfortunately, as I stops me paws suddenly becum qwite sore and I duz a hooge yelp becoz me legs mite hav fallen off. I stands qwite still and Mummy cums to see's what I's dun. Mummy sez 'Oh David'. I looks at me legs and I's leeking qwite a lot of red stuff. I's a bit worried becoz me paws are red and not me luffly brindle colour. Mummy sez me stopper pads are hanging off me legs. I's a bit worried about that becoz I wood qwite likes them on me legs proply. Mummy sez we's got to go to the vets.

Wen we gets to the vets the vet looks at me legs and says 'Oh David'. I's not sure I's very happy becoz me legs hurt but I luffs the vets becoz they calls me hansum and gives me fusses. They sez I's got to do sleeping before they can looks proply at me stopper pads. I duznt mind that becoz I woz qwite sleepies after all me running so I trots off wiv the vets and goes sleeps qwite qwickly.

Wen I wakes up I's qwite confoozed becoz I woz in a cage and me legs don't work proply and me legs has turned all blue! I sqweek becoz I wants me Mummy. So the nurses cum and gives me cuddles and sum food. I eats it all up becoz I's hungry. Then Mummy cums to gets me. The vets sez they's had to takes me stopper pads off me legs! I's sprized becoz I duznt finks they asked me if they cood hav them. I finks they's stoled them. I's also a bit worried they's swapped me legs for sumone elses becoz I's not very good at walking on these ones and I's not sure I likes me blue bandiges. Mummy has to puts me in the car. I duznt likes being picked up so I goes all stiff.

Wen we gets home I goes strayt to me bed becoz I's a bit worried about having the wrong legs on. I stays there all day but Mummy sits on the floor wiv me and I gets lots of fusses and Hooman Nanny cums and brings me lots of piggy lugs. I duz luff piggy lugs but I's not sure I wants one so I saves it in me bed for later.

Wen we goes to bed that nite I's qwite sore so me finks to tell Mummy by doing whining all nite. Mummy sez it woz alrite becoz I woz poorlies so I got to hav hextra cuddles but only on the floor becoz I coodnt get me legs on the bed.

Heventually, in the morning, I's feeling a bit better and I eats me piggy lug. I finks to meself it was qwite nice so I goes to the treet cubbord and gets the rest of the piggy lugs. Mummy finks I's a bit sneeky but sez she's pleezed I's got me appatite back. I's

not allowed walkies for ages tho!
I finks to meself not to chase the Eester Bunny agen.

Not til next Eester anyways.

I woz sad!

14th April

I's be'd to the vets agen today. I's not got to wear me bandiges anymores, wot is good. But I finks to meself, me Muvva has got confoozed. She's put one of those fings wot is on the lites on me hed. I duznt likes it. I's qwite sad. I keeps nocking me hed into fings. I's bumped into the door and the stairs and the chair. I's even on accident nocked the glass off and spilled the drink! I hopes Mummy see's I's not a lite soon! I fink she mite hav noticed I's not a lite becoz she duz say I's not very brite wot I duz finks is good.

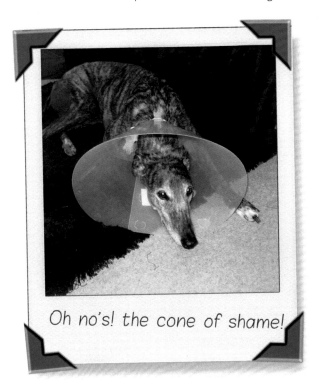

Oh no's! the cone of shame!

10th May

Resently we's been a bit warmer indoors and Mummy sez that we's not got to keep the giraffe door shut anymore. Mummy sez that giraffes don't cum in wen its warm. Anyways, I's pleezed that we's keeping the doors open agen now becoz I can play wiv me duck proply like normal and runs through to the dining room wiv out worrying about wevver I's going to runs into the door. I's been a bit worried tho in case the giraffes do cum back. I no I's never see'd one but they looks a lot bigger than me wen I sees them on telly and wot if they gets into me bed or steel me duck or eats me treets? I don't fink growling at them wood scare them away!

Last nite I forgot to do worrying about the giraffes becoz I woz having leff-dovers for tea. Once I had gobbled down me leff-dovers I picks up me duck and trots into the lounge. Me finks to kill me duck for a little while before I goes for a qwik doze in me cumfy nest bed. Well, I's playing wiv me duck wen I notice sumfing is sitting in me bed. I has to go over and hinvestigate and this is wot I found…!

A giraffe! In me bed!

I woz very brave and woznt scared at all becoz it woz not as hooge as wot I fought from the telly. Me finks to meself to feel qwite silly for finking that they wood be so big. Becoz I's not ever seen a reel giraffe before, I finks to give it a little sniff and it seems ok wiv the sniffing so I picks it up and takes it out of me bed so I can get in. As I picks the giraffe up it gives a little sqweek, like wot me teddy duz, so I frows it across the room so it no's I's boss. I has to kill it a little bit too so it duzn't cum and wakes me up in me sleeps.

Wen Mummy cums in the room, me finks to show her that we's got a giraffe in the house so she no's to keep the doors shut agen. Me finks to meself that it has to be a bit warmer before we can keep the giraffe door open uvver wise we's going to have lots of giraffes in the house!

P.S. I finks to meself to keep the giraffe, as me toy, but still finks Mummy shood make sure no more cum in. Just in case they's bigger.

i finks to luffs me giraffe

12th May

Today is Mummy's Gotcha Day! I's very luckies to hav me very own Mummy becoz lots of me frends in kennels still duznt hav their own hoo-mum or hoo-mans yet!

me muvvas gotcha day!

I can remembers the day wen I see'd me Mummy for the first time eva! They bringed me Mummy out of the car to me kennel to meets me! Wen I see'd me Mummy I gots all hexcited and dun spinning in the smallest qwickest sercles eva! I didn't hav to see's any uvva hoomans becoz I newed that woz the Mummy I's wanted! I gots to take me Mummy for walkies to makes sure I luffed walkies wiv me Mummy. I was so hexcited to be wivs me Mummy that I dun pulling on me leed til I dun choking! Mummy gived me fusses and sed as soon as they's checked the house wot we woz going to lives in then I cood takes me Mummy home! I had to do wayting ages; nearly too weeks wiv me good boy ears on before I gots to go home!

Wen I gots to me new home I had to start doing training wiv Mummy. I had to teech her how to gives me ear rubs and do me chikin and plays wiv me duck and gives me piggy lugs and takes me on long walkies to see's wabbits and sqwirrels. Then me finks to meself, praps we shood hav an hadventure! I luffs hadventures. On me hadventures I's met all me new frends! And me new frends hintroduced me Mummy to their Hoo-mums and Hoo-mans and Mummy mades new frends too! I's gots me bestest frends in the park: Ben (the dog wot goes in the water) and Bernie (who is me frend sept wen he duz barking at me) and George (who is qwite small and wabbity but wot gots the sqwirrel) and then I's got all me bestest hound frends and me luffly brindle valentine!

I's bin on sleepovas and dun working and sniffed nozes wiv ponies and dun walkies and dun barking and I's bin boating and dun showing and dun spinning and I's bin to parites and I's bin to pubs too! Wen I gots me Mummy I neva finked to meself that I wood hav haventures! Then I started to do me ritings abouts me hadventures and then I gots faymis and then I's rit a book! I's bin so bizy I has to do lots of sleeping too! I's pleezed I's picked me Mummy and I finks she's qwite pleezed I's picked her too!

Tonite, I's taking me Mummy on walkies then we's going to hav chikin, like wot I's trayned her to do on speshal days!

11th Joon

During the summer, I's a very bizy David. I takes me Mummy to helps wiv Greyhound Homer where I helps to shows peeple wot luffly pets greyhounds make wen we's 'tired from racing. I helps by taking me Mummy to shows wot Greyhound Homer is at and I duz laying down to shows them wot I duz at home. And, I duz fussing peeple and I sumtimes duz barking wen no one is doing fussing me. It is qwite hard work and I gets very sleepies but I luff to helps me frends in kennels find luffly homes and sofas like wot I's got. Sumtimes the hoomans duz making bacon rolls, sumtimes they even has sosidges! Theys me favrit and I duz sitting for leff-dovers. The peeples watching will then no's that greyhounds luffs sosidges and bacon and mite lets their greyhounds wot they takes home hav sosidges and bacon too!

Sumtimes we has to hav meetings to do talking abouts wot me next colum is abouts. Becoz I's faymis and duz ritings, I gets to sits on a chair. Me colum is qwite himportant becoz me frends needs to no's abouts wot I's doing. The hoomans do talking abouts fings too but sumtimes I duz falling asleep and duznt heers wot they's saying. Uvva times me and me frends do running in the garden!

I luffs it wen we finds homes for me frends becoz it makes me qwite sad that they's nevva dun snoozing on a sofa before or on a dubble bed. Becoz they's me favrit.

i's doing me ritings

we's doing working hard!

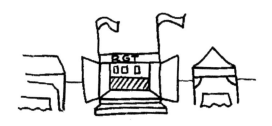

24th Joon

Me new car wot Mummy drives to takes me to see's me frends sounds difrent! Now I duznt no's wen Mummy gets home from doing working til I heers the door! Then I gets hup really qwickly and runs downstairs to do bouncing and roo-ing! I luffs it wen Mummy gets home becoz then we duz walkies wiv me park frends and then I gets me dinner!

The uvva day I woz fast asleeps on Mummy's bed and I woz dreeming of chasing wabbits becoz they woz on the telly! Suddenly, just wen me dreem woz getting really hexciting becoz I woz abouts to catch the wabbit – I heers the frunt door goes BANG! Becoz me hart neerly jumps out of me brindle, I forgets I's asleeps on the edj of the bed and I falls off and I hits me hed on the table wot is next to the bed! I woz hurt so I dun big screeming! Then I cood tastes blud! Then I did screeming sum more! Mummy runned hupstairs really qwick and sez me screem wood probly wakes the ded – wot is a bit worrying becoz I duznt wants to shares me bed wiv the ded – sumtimes ded fings sniffs funny! Wen Mummy gots to me she sed becoz of the noise wot I made she fort I's probly braked me leg or sumfing, so I showed Mummy me lip. Mummy sed

'Oh David'. Then she pulls me lip up to see's were I's cut and sez 'Oh David' agen! Mummy sez I's broked me uvva big toof! I woz a bit sprized becoz I didn't really wants to brakes me toof. Mummy dun looking for the broken bit and sez I must hav dun swallowing it

me teefs

– I don't remembers in me brain if I swallowed it so I duznt no's if it woz yummy or not. I's a bit sad that we didn't finds it becoz I cood hav puts it under me pillow for the toof fairy to takes away and she wood hav left me treet munnie! I's going to keeps looking.

Now I's got two broken big teefs. I hopes it duznt makes catching sqwirrels more difficult becoz they's qwite hard to catch anyways!

5th July

This weekend I it woz hot! We wents to Hooman Nanny's house to eats outside food cooked on fire! Hooman Nanny's garden is luffly and big for running but it woz too hot to do proper running. I just dun lots of sniffing and snuffling becoz theys got hej-hogs and wabbits and foxes and sqwirrels and deers in their garden and their poos all sniffs luffly! Becoz of all the sniffs I's had to makes sure that I's smelled effry plant and effry stone. I has a good sniff of the green stuff and then tests a bit wiv me teefs. Wen I takes a little brake from me sniffing Mummy takes a pikture of me looking all hansum. Wen I sees the picture I's qwite sprized becoz most of me luffly brindle colour woz missing! I woz wite!

 I gets meself qwite worried becoz I cant remembers it falling off so I has to go looks for it! I has to do a speshal hinvestigashon of the garden. I has to go back to all the plants I's sniffed and sniffs them agen, just in case me luffly brindle colour woz there, but I didn't sees it. I checks the plants, I checks the firey tin fing for cooking outside food, and I checks the kitchen and the sofa. I even checks Roger in case he's stolen me brindle!

Once I's checked Roger, I turns around and sees me reflekshon in the window. Me brindle woz back! I's really pleezed. It must hav got back on me wen I woz hinvestigating! I's going to be more careful in future not to loose me brindle wen I's sniffing in Hooman Nanny's garden.

i's wite!!

looking for me brindle in the plants

is me brindle in the fire food cooker?

17th July

This weekend I's bin on an hadventure! I's bin to see's me frends Lynx and Lou wiv Ella and we's bin on a boat! We wents to Lou and Lynx's house before we dun going on the boat! They's gots a hooge garden and becoz I woz sooper hexcited and had energies in me legs I dun running around the garden really fast wiv Lynx. I dun sniffing and snuffling and I woz qwite bizy checking all the grass! Suddenly wen I woz doing running round the garden I went splash! I didn't luffs going splash and I puts me sad face on! The grass had dun changing to water! I woz in the pond! I duznt luffs water becoz it mites wash me luffly brindle colour off so I gots out of the pond really qwick and dun a big shake to gets the water out of me good boy ears (wot I woznt wearing becoz I woz wet)! Fankfully Lynx's Mummy see'd me all wet and gots a big towel out to rubs me dry before me brindle cood wash away. All the hoomans sed 'Oh David' and I felts a bit sillies but I still dun more sniffing and snuffling.

Soon we woz on the boat. Ella woz qwite sleepies from all the sniffing in the garden and dun sleeping but I dun hinvestigating all the beds and the boat! Lou showed me wot I woz meant to do and dun laying down but I woz too hexcited to do laying down so Lynx showed me how to do looking. I luffed doing looking! I cood see's all the ducks and cood sniffs them on wind! I cood see's all the peeple and they woz looking at me so I puts me best good boy ears on and dun barking! I dun lots of barking so the peeple wood no's that I woz here!

me frends

Wen we stopped to do locks, Lou and Lynx gots off. I wanted to gets off to help too! Mummy sez I's got to calms down a little bits first but I's still very hexcited. I finks Mummy and Ella's Hu-mum were a bit worred abouts me doing jumping into the water (even though I duznt luffs water!) so I had to wears a silly oranj coat wot cuvvered hup me brindle! Then I woz allowed to do helping wiv Lynx. Lynx dun wee's on a tree, so I dun helping and dun wee's on the tree too! Then Lynx dun wee's on a rock, so I dun helping and dun wee's on the rock too!

Heventually sum of me energies gots used up and I wents to sit on the sofa. I didn't wants to do sleeping though just in case sumfing hexciting happened and me eyes were shut, so I tried me best to keeps them open.

All of a sudden wen me eyes were just abouts to do closing, I heers peeple shouting 'oooo aarrrr'! I woz qwite sprized and qwickly wents outside to see's wot woz happening. There woz pirates! I's neva see'd a reel pirate before sept in the tellyvision. They's qwite scary. We had to go rites up close to them in the lock and they woz on top of the boat! They's got sords! They woz shouting and jumping and doing drinking from bottles (I spect it woz rum becoz that's wot pirates drink; I no's this becoz I's see'd it in the telly)!

I woz hexcited to see's the pirates but I woz pleezed I didn't havs me duck wiv me becoz wood probly taked him as trezure!

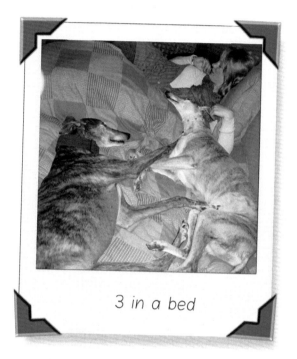

3 in a bed

Wen the pirates coodnt see's us anymore, Lynx's Daddy dun parking the boat and we dun walking around a market! There woz lots of peeple and they dun fussing me and Ella and Lynx and Lou becoz we's all luffly.

Lou, me and Lynx

I didn't finks they no'd I woz David tho, becoz sum of them had to ask me Mummy me name. In the market one man didn't luffs us very much and sed we woznt allowed to be in the market becoz we's agenst elf and safety. I's nevva mets an elf before so I tells the man that I's not agesnt elfs and I's qwite safe becoz Mummy made me wears the silly oranj coat! But the man didn't do listening to me and we had to goes back to the boat. I woz sad becoz all the peoples sed we woz luffly and were doing fussing me and me frends. I woz qwite sleepies so wen we gots back I dun snoozings and I gots to do snoozing next to me luffly Ella!

In the morning, wen the boat woz doing moving agen we gots to lays on the beds outside becoz the sun woz back in the sky! I woz qwite wored out. Becoz I woz so wored out Mummy sed I didn't have to wears the oranj coat. I woz qwite pleezed becoz all the peeple cood see's me luffly brindle colour! I luffs to do sunbathing! Even Ella cames and dun sunbathing and looking wiv us!

We's had a luffly weekend (sept wen I went spash in the pond!) and I's hexzoorsted. Wen we gots home last nite I wents strayt to me bed and dun sleeping! I wood luffs to do looking on a boat wiv me new frends Lou and Lynx agen!

13th Orgust

Today there woz lots of rain. We's had to do walkies very qwickly becoz I duznt luffs to get wet. I worrys me luffly brindle colour will wash off. I's lost me luffly brindle colour on me toes becoz of the puddles and becoz me coat duznt cuvver me face me luffly brindle colour is washing off there too and I's going grey! Becoz walkies woz qwite qwick I's still had lots of energies in me legs so I's been killing me duck and frowing me duck and plucking me duck. They's me favrit games wiv me duck. I duz have a little cuddle wiv Mummy in the evenin but me energies don't let me legs do laying down for very long. So I kills me duck all ova agen and then I kills teddy too, wiv me teefs!

Wen its bed time, Mummy puts me out for wee's. I has to do wee's really qwickly becoz Mummy duznt puts me coat on me wen I duz wees and I's still duz worrying about me brindle in the rain. I runs down the garden really qwickly and I's qwite sprized wen i suddenly duz slipping ova! The grass had gone slippery and me legs finks to go sumwhere I didn't wants them too so I felled on me side! Wen I gots up I finks to do wee's really qwickly just incase the grass makes me legs do funny fings agen and then I runs indoors. I shows Mummy that I's falled ova in the mud and Mummy sez 'Oh David'. Wen I looked at me luffly brindle colour I sees that I's all cuvvered in mud! Mummy sed I needs to hav a barf before I goes to bed. I duznt wants to hav a barf just incase Mummy washed me brindle off by acsident so wen Mummy tries to picks me up and puts me in the barf I goes all stiff and sticks me legs out so Mummy cant lifts me up.

i duz not luffs to be wet

Even tho I woz being stiff Mummy still managed to puts me in the barf and I didn't luffs it very much but I stood still like wot good boys do and lets Mummy gets the mud off me brindle. Wen I woz all washed Mummy sed she needs to gets me out of the barf. Me finks to meself I cood jumps out of the barf meself, so I tries to jumps out and me legs do fings I duznt wants them too and I goes slipping ova agen and I hurts me chin on the side of the barf. I woz qwite worried abouts doing slipping ova wen I stands up so me finks to meself to lays down in the barf and waits for Mummy to lifts me out. Mummy sez I's being silly and I needs to do standing up so she can gets me out but I didn't wants to do standing up becoz of me legs doing slipping. Mummy goes to the treet cubbord to gets sum treets so that if I's a good boy and stands up I can hav one. They woz nice treets but I woz too worried abouts me legs to gets up so Mummy gets sum even nicer treets out of the cubbord. They woz nice sniffing treets to but I still didn't wants to stand up in the barf. Mummy sez 'rite then David, you's going to hav to stays in the barf all nite' and then wents to the fridge and made the cheeze make noize. I didn't wants to stays in the barf all nite and I duz luffs cheese, its me favrit but I coodnt go and sits in the cheeze spot and puts me good boy ears on becoz I woz in the barf.

Me finks to meself I shood gets out of the barf and goes and do sitting for the cheeze. So, I jumps strayt out of the barf and goes to the kitchen. Mummy sez I's a good boy and gives me a hooge bit of cheeze and i didn't even gets time to put me good boy ears on!

Wen we goes upstairs Mummy gives me a big rub wiv a towel to gets all the water out of me brindle so it duznt dizolve and puts me jarmies on to keeps me warm. Then I dun curling up in me cozee nest bed and goes to sleep. Me finks to meself to be qwite carefuls in the garden in the rain in future.

20th Orgust

Yesterdie on walkies I woz qwite hembarrassed. We woz doing walkies down a new road! I duz luffs to go walkies new places becoz of the sniffs! I did sniffing the plants and I did sniffing the trees and I did sniffing the grass! Then I sees there woz two cats! They woz sitting very stills on top of the wall! I gots very hexcited and dun spinning and whinging and barking! We gots closer to the cats but they stayed very still. Usually cats do running away from me very qwickly and duznt wants to stay to do playing wiv me, wot is sad, so I gots more hexcited becoz I mite be able to plays wiv them!

Wen we woz rite up close to the cats they woz still there doing sitting very still and me finks to do playing wiv them so I dun spinning and then I dun pouncing! I jumped hup really high and landed on the first cat! I woz qwite sprized becoz the cat woz hard! It woz made of stone! I's neva see'd a cat made of stone before. The cat made me hurts me leg a little and I's leeked a little red stuff but I didn't mind becoz the uvva cat woz still sitting very still on the uvva wall so I dun spinning agen and dun anuvva hooge pounce and jumped onto the cat! The uvva cat didn't do moving either and it woz very hard and dun hurting me too, I's bit me tung! Two stone cats! I's neva see'd two stone cats before! Mummy sez I woz qwite sillys and wen we gots home I had to hav me leg washed were I woz leeking red stuff. Then i curled up in me bed and feels qwite sorrys for meself for being so sillies!

dreeming ...

18th Septemba

Last nite wen we wents to bed it woz qwite cold. I kepts doing fijeting and whining and asking to gets on Mummy's bed to keeps warm. Mummy sez I duz too much fijeting wen I's asleeps to do sleeping on the bed so goes to gets me jarmies. Wen Mummy looks in me jarmies cubbord she me jarmies are not there. 'Oh no's' sez Mummy, 'they must be at Hooman Nanny's house'. Oh no's me finks, I's going to be colds all nite! I goes to me bed and puts me cold face on so Mummy goes to finds a blankit to cuvvers me up wiv and we goes back to sleep. The blankit woz okies but wen I duz chasing the wabbits in me sleeps the blankit cums off so I has to do sqweeking agen and asking to gets on Mummy's bed. Then, Mummy finks in her brain, praps I cood wears one of her t-shirts to keeps me warm. Mummy pops me frunt legs in the holes wot her arms goes in and then we goes back to sleeps. I's feeling much more cozee and warm. Suddenly, wen I's fast asleeps, I finks to meself that the t-shirt has dun eating one of me back legs. I tries to gets me leg out of the t-shirt but I cants, its eated me leg all up! I's qwite worried abouts this so I duz screeming qwite loud so Mummy wakes up qwite qwickly. Wen Mummy wakes up she see's that the t-shirt has et one of me back legs and sez 'Oh David'.

I duz more screeming becoz I duznt wants to only hav free legs! Mummy qwickly rescues me leg from the t-shirt and sez its becoz I's dun dreeming and running after wabbits that me legs gots stuck.
I duznt wants to puts the t-shirt on agen anymores so Mummy sez I's going to havs to gets on the bed and do sleeping wiv her.

heventually, i gots to do sleeping in mummy's bed!

I's very pleezed the t-shirt dun eating me leg becoz I snuggled rite up close wiv Mummy all nite! We's going to hav to gets me jarmies back from Hooman Nannys house tomoro!

28th Septemba

Today is Mummy's berfdie! I's had a berfdie before too and I gots prezants! Becoz I's not allowed to go to the shops on me own I finks to meself I's going to hav to makes me Mummy a speshal prezant for her berfdie! I gives her lots of berfdie hugs so she no's I's not forgotten in me brain that its her berfdie and then I goes to curl up in me bed wiv me kong wen Mummy goes to do working.

Wen I's finished me kong I finks to meself to starts to make Mummy's speshal prezant so I duz wandering around to finks of wot speshal fings I cood do. Wen I wanders into the dining room I see's the kitshen door is opens just enuff to gets meself froo! So I trots in the kitshen and finks to meself that I cood makes Mummy a speshal tea! I finks to meself that me favrit is leff-dovers. Wen we's finished doing eating I remembers that the leff-dovers that we's not going to eats are puts in the bin. I luffs to sniffs the bin but Mummy sez 'no' becoz I's not allowed in the bin. I finks to meself that Mummy woodn't mind this time becoz I's making a speshal prezant for her berfdie.

So I puts me noze in the bin wiv all the luffly sniffs and pulls out the leff-dovers. I takes them into the dining room where Mummy usually duz eating and puts them on the floor. Then I goes and takes more leff-dovers and puts them on the floor too! I makes such luffly leff-dovers on the floor I gets qwite sleepies so me finks to go and hav a sleeps before Mummy gets home from doing working.

waiting for muvva

I runs upstairs and jumps on the bed. Then I finks to meself praps Mummy wood luffs it if I makes her bed smells all like me becoz I luffs the bed wen it sniffs all like her. So, I digs all the cuvvers up and duz turning round and rubbing all ova the bed. I finks to meself that Mummy wood be very pleezed wiv the leff-dover tea and me luffly smelly bed so I goes to sleeps.

i's dun helping!

Wen Mummy gets home from doing working I runs to the door really qwickly and duz me best barking and me best good boy ears and me best jumping! Then I runs froo to the dining room to shows Mummy her tea! Leff-dovers! Mummy woznt qwite as happy as wot I fought she wood be and she duz picking the leff-dovers back hup and putting them in the bin agen! Mummy sez that we's having fish and chips for tea insted of leff-dovers! They's me favrit too!

Wen we wents up to bed Mummy see'd me luffly cozee bed wot I had made her. She woz very pleezed and sed that I shood gets on the bed and do sleeping wiv her all nite becoz I's such a good boy! I woz very pleezed too and we dun luffly snugglings!

1st Octoba

Today, is me berfdie. Mummy sez I woz borned in too-fousand-and-too! Becoz its me berfdie I's got prezants! I's very hexcited abouts me prezants. Me favrit prezant I's eva gots for me berfdie woz me duck! Me duck is the bestest! I duz playing wiv me duck and frowing me duck and plucking me duck and tugging me duck!

For me berfdie this year, I's got piggy lugs and a sqweeky blob! I luffs the sqweeky blob! I makes it go sqweek wen I kills it. I's dun running around wiv it and I's got lots of energies. Once I's killed me blob. Mummy tooked me for walkies. We had hextra long walkies to the beech wiv me frends! I's sniffed their bottoms and then we sniffed nozes! I luffs the beech and sumtimes if its windy I finks the see-weed is a wabbit and duz spinning and barking becoz I wants to do chasing it! Even tho it woz me berfdie Mummy still didn't lets me to chasing the see-weed. I made sure I dun lots of hextra speshal berfdie wee's on all the beech grass wot duz growing in the sand. Me frends all dun paddling in the see but I duznt wants the see to wash me luffly brindle colour off so I duznt goes in wiv them. I just duz barking at them on the sand!

Wen we gots home from walkies I woz qwite hexzoorsted and I gobbled me speshal berfdie fishy and rice up very qwickly so I cood do snoozing. But before I cood go do snoozing, Mummy brought me out me own speshal cake! I luffs cake! Its one of me favrits! Mummy singed 'happy berfdie to you, happy berfdie to you, happy berfie deer David, happy berfdie too you!' I luffed me own speshal song and wagged me tail lots and I dun gobbling me cake up. Then I dun sleeping. I dun dreeming of chasing the see-weed on the beech.

berfdie cake!
me favrit

20th Octoba

Oh no's I's had anuvva acsident! I woz in the park and I woz running! I woz doing running really fast becoz I duz luffs to run. Suddenly wen I woz running I feels a bit sore on one of me feets I finks to meself to stops running just for a bits.

Mummy camed to see if I woz alrite but I didn't wants Mummy to looks at me feet just in case I has to go back on me leed so I duz running agen.

Wen we gets home after running I duz laying down and me foot feels qwite sore so I duz licking it. Wen Mummy sees I's licking me foot she makes me shows her wot I's dun. Wen I shows her Mummy sez 'Oh David'. I looks at me foot and I see's

anuvva bandij!

I's got a hole between me toes! I woz qwite sprized. Mummy sez I shood probly go to the vets to gets them to looks at me poorly paw. I luffs the vets so i gets qwite hexcited and duz spinning then I remember me paw hurts me so I stops spinning and lifts me paw up.

Wen we gets to the vets the vet sez 'Oh David' too! I finks to meself praps its me new name. The vet sez I's got to hav stitches in me paw becoz of the hole and I's going to hav to be asleeps wen they puts me back togevva. I duznt mind going to sleeps becoz I woz qwite sleepies from all me running so I goes wiv the vet to me speshal bed at the vets.

Wen I wakes up I's got a hooge bandige on me paw and I's feeling all wobbly and me legs aren't doing walking how they's sposed to. Wen I sees Mummy I wags me tail but me legs are doing wobbling so much I falls ova! Mummy has to do carrying me to the car and then to me bed wen we gets home! I woz qwite sleepies and did sleeping all afternoon sept for wen it woz tea time. Becoz I woz poorlies I gots to hav chikin and rice wot is one of me favrits! I did wobbling to me food bowl and ates it all up really qwickly! Then I wents back to sleeps agen. Me finks to trys to be more carefuls wen I's running next time!

3rd Novemba

Suddenly last nite wen I woz doing sleeping in me bed, the varz
that woz on the window sill dun jumping on me! I woznt even doing
dreeming or wagging me tail or watching the cats! I woz asleeps!
And it did jumping on me! Becoz I woz qwite sprized to sees the
varz doing jumping on me, I finks to screem qwite loud to wakes
me Mummy up. I finks Mummy woz qwite sprized to hears me
screem to and gets up very qwickly to see's wot is wrong wiv me!
Wen she see's that the varz is in me bed Mummy sez that it must
be a goat wot nocked it off the window sill. I's sprized by that
too becoz I's not see'd any goats. I woz qwite worried, I's only
just made the giraffe me frend, I duznt wants to hav to shares
me bed wiv a goat too! Mummy sez its ok though becoz you can
hexercise fings wot are haunted by goats and then they goes away!
I's pleezed we can gets rid of the goat just by taking the varz
walkies. Mummy puts the varz back on the window sill and we goes
back to sleeps for a little while.

Wen we wakes up I's looking forward to walkies wiv the varz so
that we can gets rid of the goat. I spect praps the goat lives
in the varz. Mummy sez I's silly to takes the varz wivs us but me

i's wayting for the goat to cums out

finks how we's going to hexercise it if we duznt take it walkies! So Mummy pops the varz wot has the goat living in it in her bag and we goes to the park! I luffs the park and I dun sniffing and snuffling! I dun sniffing and snuffling so much I forgots to watch Mummy's bag to sees if the goat came out of the varz. I finks to meself it must hav come out of the varz becoz of all the luffly sniffs. Wen we gets home Mummy shows me the varz and I can see's that the goat isn't inside anymore. I's qwite pleezed we's hexercised the goat! Mummy pops the varz backs in its place above me bed, but I duznt mind becoz I don't finks the goat will come back becoz it is in the park, wiv the sniffs and snuffles.

23rd Novemba

Today, after tea Mummy went upstairs to makes the bed so me finks to curls up on me sofa for a snooze. Wen I's doing snoozing I finks to meself I hears sumfing in the kitchen. I goes to hinvestigate and discuvver that there woz a feef in the house who had stole sum cheese and sum creem and had chewed on the milk bottle to gets the drips.

I no's wot this picture looks like but I's really searching for hevidence to see who the food feef woz.

Wen I woz hinvestigating I's found some black fluff and some ginger fluffs and I cood sniffs sumfing rather houndy. I finks to meself that the feef woz a big brindle greyhound. Good job I woz asleeps on the sofa wen the feefery took place!

i didn't eats it, i woz
hinvestigating!

is the feef doing hiding in
the cubbord?

1st Decemba

Deer Santa Claws

I's sending you me ritings of me fings wot I wood qwite likes for Crismiss. I no's I's dun a few mischiffs this year but I's not be'd norty sept on accident sumtimes. Like wen the sosidges jumped in to me mouth. That woz on accident! I's even remembered that you's not allowed to do wee's on the Crismiss tree, but I still finks to meself that its silly to hav a indoor tree wot you cant do wee's on! I's dun all me wee's outside!

So becoz I's be'd such a good boy and dun helping at home and at shows wood you pleeze brings me:

- Lots of piggy lugs, becoz they's me favrit!
- A nuvva cozee nest bed for the barfroom so I can lays down wen I's watching wot peeples are doing in there.
- A speshal hooman bed all of me own for the room wiv out a bed. I wood luffs to hav me own speshal hooman bed to do sleeping in wen Mummy takes up all of the room in me bedroom! I no's this is qwite big and mite not fit on your sley so I don't mind

not having the cozee nest bed for the barfroom if me speshal hooman bed will fits in your sley then!

- I wood also likes, if I's be'd good enuff, the wrascally meerkat from the telly. I qwite likes him and I finks to meself he wood be qwite good to sqweek.

I really wants to see's you on Crismiss Eve wen you cums down the chimney, speshally becoz I wants to gives you a little sniff, but you's probly going to cums after me bed time and I will be fast asleeps. Praps I will gets to sniff you next year!
Lots of luffs,

David

P.S. Pleeze Santa Claws, can I hav anuvva diary for next year so I can still makes me ritings of me mischiffs.
P.P.S. I's put me big red sock by the chimney becoz its wot they duz on telly. I don't no's if you will fits me speshal hooman bed in there so can you puts it in the bedroom wot duznt hav a bed in it. Fank you.

25th Decemba

i's wayting for santa claws

I's very hexcited this morning! Today is Crismiss Day! I's doing bouncing sooper high so Mummy will gets up qwickly so we can see's if I woz good enuff to gets fings from Santa Claws. Mummy sez I's got to go downstairs before I can looks in the room wot duznt hav a bed in it, so I goes downstairs very qwickly.

I forgets about Santa Claws for a little wile and duz bouncing for me brekfst so Mummy makes me brekfst first. Then she sez about Santa Claws and I remembers in me brain, that it's Crismiss day and I mite hav fings in me big red sock.

Wen I see'd me sock in the frunt room I see's that I's got lots of luffly fings in it. Sum sez they's from Roodolf and sum say they's from Santa Claws. One woz from Hooman Nanny. That woz treets. I duz luff treets. Theys sum of me favrits! Then Mummy sez there's a speshal prezant for me hupstairs. I's qwite hexcited becoz I luffs speshal prezants. I goes hupstairs wiv Mummy very qwickly and bangs me noze on the door to the bedroom wot duznt have a bed in it becoz I forgots to see's that the door woz shut! I duz whining a little bit just in case I's hurt but I woznt and Mummy gived me a qwick cuddle before she opens the door.

I trots in and I see's a speshal hooman bed! Mummy sez its for me becoz I's such a good boy! I's so hexcited I puts me good boy ears on and jumps rite up on to all the cushons and blankets! I has a little roll about and makes meself all cumfee and cozee.

i luffs prezants!

Wen I's dun having a little snooze on me new speshal bed we goes walkies to the park where I see's me frends! I gives them a speshal crismiss day sniff and they sniffs me bottom too!

For dinner, becoz its Crismiss I gets speshal dinner wot isn't leff-dovers! I gets it made speshal! Its turkey wiv vejtables. Its one of me favrits. Then for tea I gets ham!

I's qwite full and sleepy after me bizzy day so I goes hupstairs to me new speshal hooman bed. Mummy cums to gives me a little cuddle so I gives her a cuddle to says fank you for me luffly speshal bed.

I duz luffs Crismiss. I finks its one of me favrits too! I finks I's a very lucky brindle greyhound!

me luffly new bed!

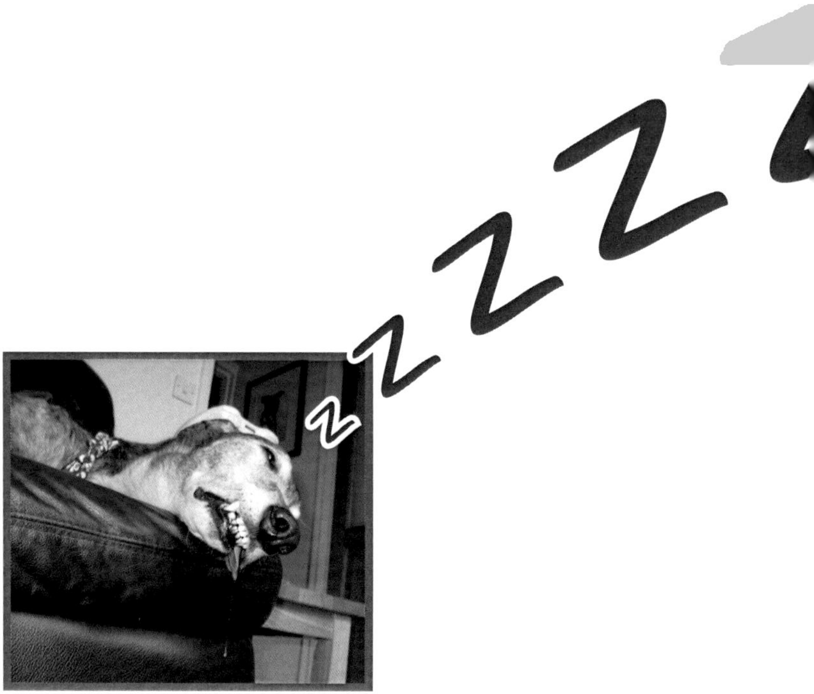

If you luffed me ritings you can follow me on me blog, me Facebook and me Twitter. (I's a very sociable hound)

Me blog is at:

www.davidsbestmate.blogspot.com

A lot of the munies from me ritings
will goes to helps greyhounds
evrywhere wot is still in kennels
wayting for their foreva homes.

There are many organisations and individuals who do fantastic work helping to find homes for retired greyhounds all over the world.

We especially admire the work of those people helping Spanish greyhounds, Galgos. one of many such organisations is Greyhounds in Need (GIN). Their website is **www.greyhoundsinneed.co.uk**

In the UK, The Retired Greyhound Trust (RGT) has branches all over the country. For details of your local branch please see **www.retiredgreyhounds.co.uk**.

Charitable organisations can purchase stocks of this book for onward sale. Please contact us at davids.staff@gmail.com for more details.